C000297739

HOME ORGANIST LIBRARY VOLUME 13

Classical Themes

Arranged by Kenneth Baker.

Wise Publications
London/New York/Paris/Sydney

Exclusive Distributors:
Music Sales Limited
8/9 Frith Street, London W1V 5TZ, England.
Music Sales Pty Limited
120 Rothschild Avenue, Rosebery, NSW 2018, Australia.

This book © Copyright 1992 by Wise Publications
Order No.AM88924
ISBN 0-7119-2963-7

Designed by Howard Brown
Cover Photograph by Holly Warburton
Compiled by Peter Evans
Music arranged by Kenneth Baker
Music processed by MSS Studios

Music Sales' complete catalogue lists thousands of titles
and is free from your local music shop, or direct from Music Sales Limited.
Please send a cheque/postal order for £1.50 for postage to:
Music Sales Limited, Newmarket Road, Bury St Edmunds, Suffolk IP33 3YB.

Your Guarantee of Quality.
As publishers, we strive to produce every book to the highest commercial standards.
The music has been freshly engraved and the book has been carefully designed to minimise
awkward page turns and to make playing from it a real pleasure.
Particular care has been given to specifying acid-free, neutral-sized paper which has not been
chlorine bleached but produced with special regard for the environment.
Throughout, the printing and binding have been planned to ensure a sturdy, attractive publication
which should give years of enjoyment.
If your copy fails to meet our high standards, please inform us and we will gladly replace it.

Unauthorised reproduction of any part of this publication by any
means including photocopying is an infringement of copyright.

Printed in the United Kingdom by
JB Offset Printers (Marks Tey) Limited, Marks Tey, Essex.

Contents:

Symphony No.1

Composed by Johannes Brahms.

© Copyright 1992 Dorsey Brothers Music Limited, 8/9 Frith Street, London W1.
All Rights Reserved. International Copyright Secured.

stop drums 5

Violin Concerto

Composed by Felix Mendelssohn.

© Copyright 1992 Dorsey Brothers Music Limited, 8/9 Frith Street, London W1.
All Rights Reserved. International Copyright Secured.

8

Romeo And Juliet

Composed by Peter Ilyich Tchaikovsky.

Upper: horn
Lower: flutes
Pedal: 16' + 8'
Drums: off

© Copyright 1992 Dorsey Brothers Music Limited, 8/9 Frith Street, London W1.
All Rights Reserved. International Copyright Secured.

Scheherazade

Composed by N A Rimsky-Korsakov.

Upper: violin solo
Lower: flutes
Pedal: 16' + 8'
Drums: off

© Copyright 1992 Dorsey Brothers Music Limited, 8/9 Frith Street, London W1.
All Rights Reserved. International Copyright Secured.

Polovtsian Dances

Composed by Alexander Borodin.

Upper: oboe
Lower: flutes
Pedal: 8'
Drums: bossa nova

© Copyright 1992 Dorsey Brothers Music Limited, 8/9 Frith Street, London W1.
All Rights Reserved. International Copyright Secured.

stop drums

Land Of Hope & Glory

Composed by Sir Edward Elgar.

Upper: trumpet
Lower: flutes + strings
Pedal: 16' + 8'
Drums: march ($\frac{2}{4}$ or $\frac{4}{4}$)

© Copyright 1992 Dorsey Brothers Music Limited, 8/9 Frith Street, London W1.
All Rights Reserved. International Copyright Secured.

stop drums

Pastoral Symphony

Composed by Ludwig Van Beethoven.

Upper: string ensemble
Lower: flutes
Pedal: 16′ + 8′
Drums: waltz (or off)

© Copyright 1992 Dorsey Brothers Music Limited, 8/9 Frith Street, London W1.
All Rights Reserved. International Copyright Secured.

stop drums

22

Piano Concerto

Composed by Edvard Grieg.

Upper: piano
Lower: flutes + strings
Pedal: 16' + 8'
Drums: off

© Copyright 1992 Dorsey Brothers Music Limited, 8/9 Frith Street, London W1.
All Rights Reserved. International Copyright Secured.

Jupiter

(from 'The Planets Suite')

Composed by Gustav Holst.

Upper: string ensemble
Lower: flutes
Pedal: 8'
Drums: waltz (or off)

© Copyright 1923 J. Curwen & Sons Limited, 8/9 Frith Street, London W1V 5TZ.
All Rights Reserved. International Copyright Secured.

The Unfinished Symphony

Composed by Franz Schubert.

Upper: cello
Lower: flutes
Pedal: 16′ + 8′
Drums: off

♩ = 100

© Copyright 1992 Dorsey Brothers Music Limited, 8/9 Frith Street, London W1.
All Rights Reserved. International Copyright Secured.

Dance Of The Hours

(from 'La Gioconda')

Composed by Amilcare Ponchielli.

Upper: clarinet
Lower: flutes
Pedal: 8′
Drums: off

© Copyright 1992 Dorsey Brothers Music Limited, 8/9 Frith Street, London W1.
All Rights Reserved. International Copyright Secured.

The Merry Wives Of Windsor Overture

Composed by Karl Nicolai.

Upper: string ensemble
Lower: flutes
Pedal: 8'
Drums: 8 beat

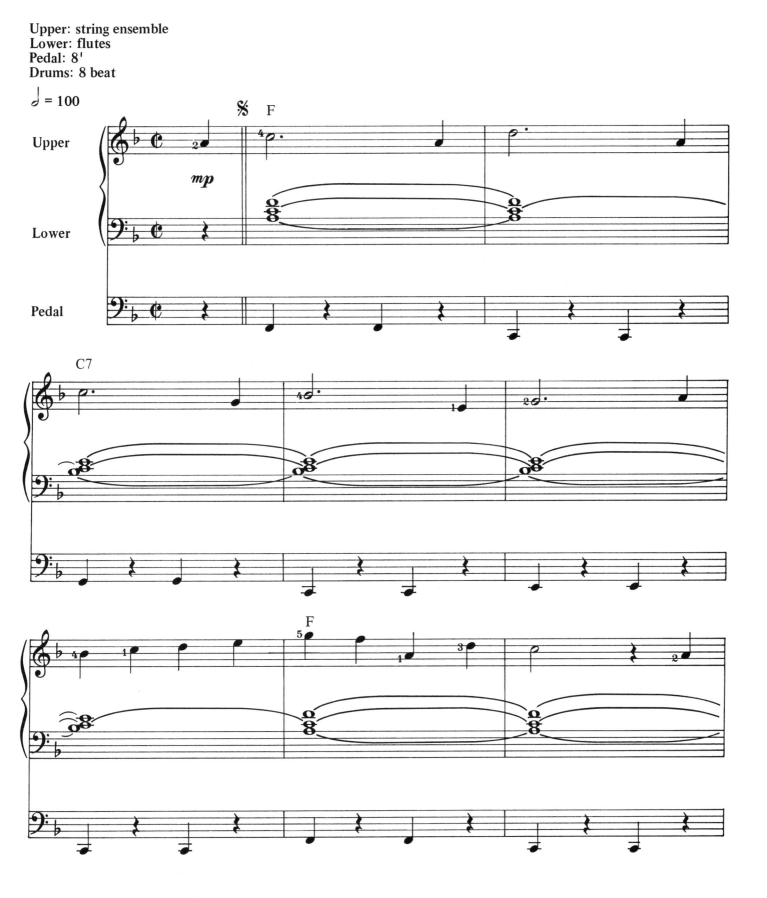

© Copyright 1992 Dorsey Brothers Music Limited, 8/9 Frith Street, London W1.
All Rights Reserved. International Copyright Secured.

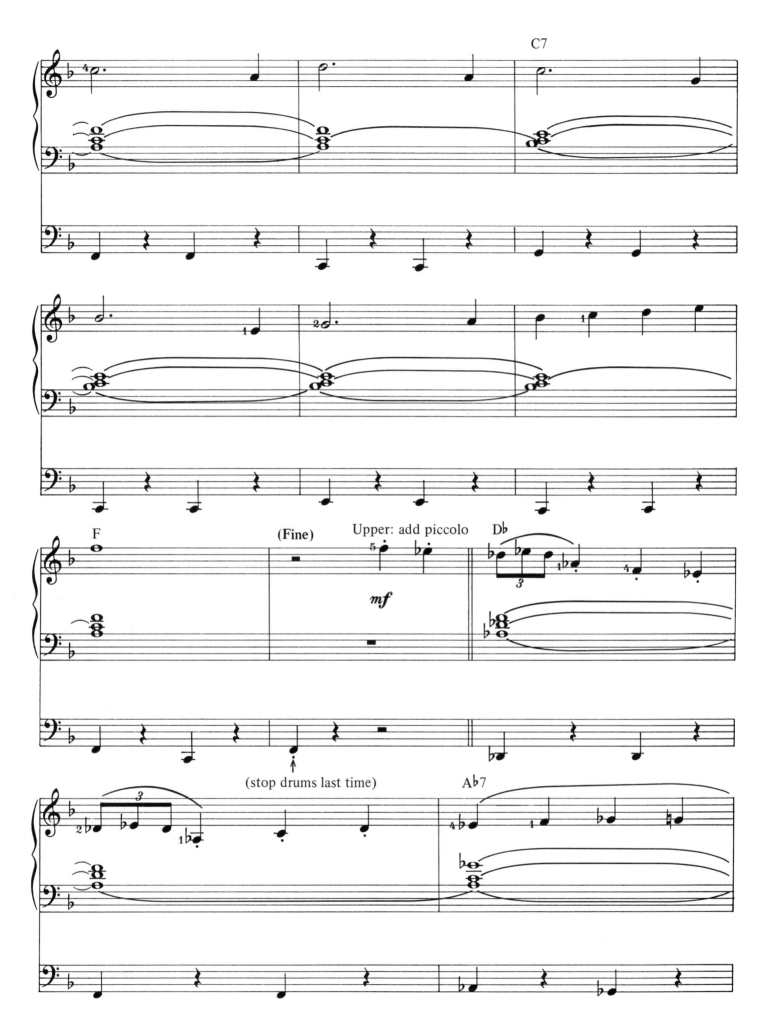

Piano Concerto No.1

Composed by Peter Ilyich Tchaikovsky.

Upper: piano
Lower: flutes + piano
Pedal: 16′ + 8′
Drums: waltz

© Copyright 1992 Dorsey Brothers Music Limited, 8/9 Frith Street, London W1.
All Rights Reserved. International Copyright Secured.

stop drums

Nocturne

Composed by Alexander Borodin.

© Copyright 1992 Dorsey Brothers Music Limited, 8/9 Frith Street, London W1.
All Rights Reserved. International Copyright Secured.

Rosamunde Overture

Composed by Franz Schubert.

Upper: clarinet
Lower: flutes + strings
Pedal: 16′ + 8′
Drums: 8 beat

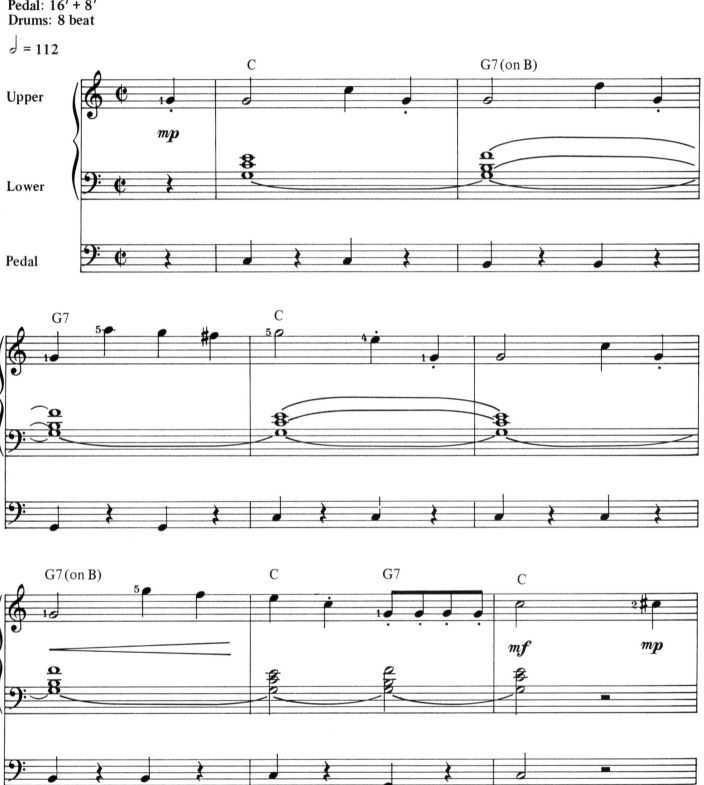

40

© Copyright 1992 Dorsey Brothers Music Limited, 8/9 Frith Street, London W1.
All Rights Reserved. International Copyright Secured.

stop drums

43

Spartacus

Composed by Aram Khachaturian.

Upper: string ensemble
Lower: flutes + horn
Pedal: 8^l
Drums: bossa nova

© Copyright 1992 Dorsey Brothers Music Limited, 8/9 Frith Street, London W1.
All Rights Reserved. International Copyright Secured.

stop drums

Scherzo

Composed by Henry Litolff.

Upper: piano
Lower: flutes + strings
Pedal: 8'
Drums: waltz (or off)

© Copyright 1992 Dorsey Brothers Music Limited, 8/9 Frith Street, London W1.
All Rights Reserved. International Copyright Secured.

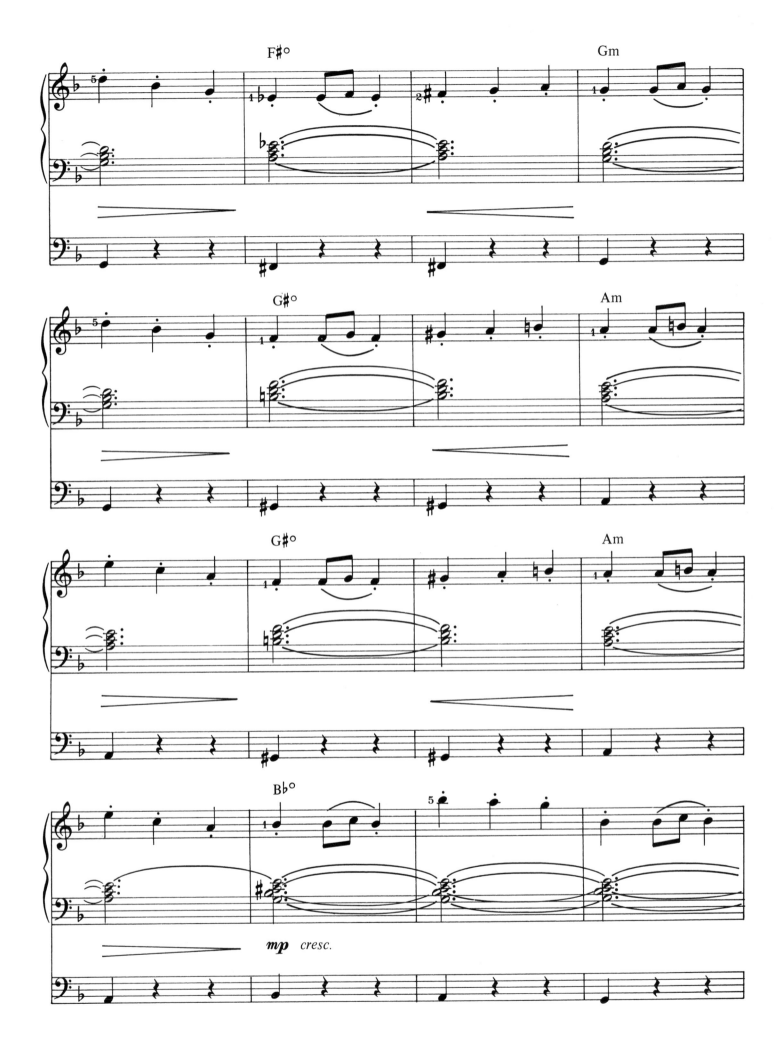

D.C. al Coda

⊕ CODA

stop drums

Chorus Of The Hebrew Slaves

Composed by Giuseppe Verdi.

Upper: clarinet
Lower: flutes
Pedal: 16^I + 8^I
Drums: slow rock

© Copyright 1992 Dorsey Brothers Music Limited, 8/9 Frith Street, London W1.
All Rights Reserved. International Copyright Secured.

stop drums

The Barber Of Seville

Composed by Gioacchino Rossini.

Upper: oboe + flute
Lower: flutes + piano
Pedal: 8'
Drums: 8 beat

© Copyright 1992 Dorsey Brothers Music Limited, 8/9 Frith Street, London W1.
All Rights Reserved. International Copyright Secured.

Upper: oboe and flute
to clarinet

stop
drums

Swan Lake

Composed by Peter Ilyich Tchaikovsky.

Upper: oboe
Lower: flutes
Pedal: 16′ + 8′
Drums: off

© Copyright 1992 Dorsey Brothers Music Limited, 8/9 Frith Street, London W1.
All Rights Reserved. International Copyright Secured.

Spring

(from 'The Four Seasons')

By Antonio Vivaldi.

Upper: harpsichord
Lower: flutes
Pedal: 8'
Drums: 8 beat (or off)

1. SPRING

© Copyright 1992 Dorsey Brothers Music Limited, 8/9 Frith Street, London W1.
All Rights Reserved. International Copyright Secured.

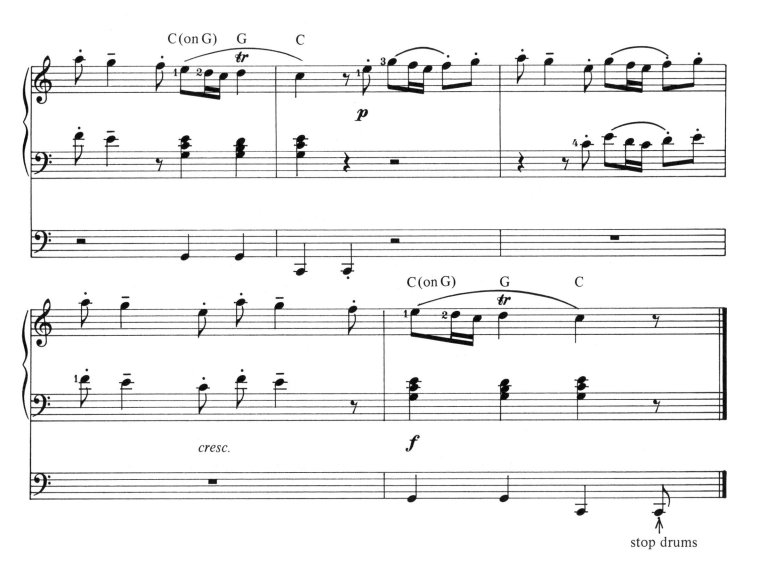

2. AUTUMN

Upper: flute
Lower: flutes
Pedal: 16' + 8'
Drums: waltz (or off)

♩ = 126

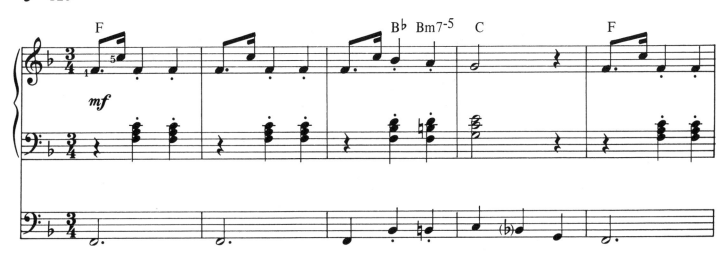

Upper: add flute

mp

cresc.

f

stop drums

Symphony No.40

Composed by Wolfgang Amadeus Mozart.

Upper: string ensemble
Lower: flutes
Pedal: 16^l + 8^l
Drums: 8 beat

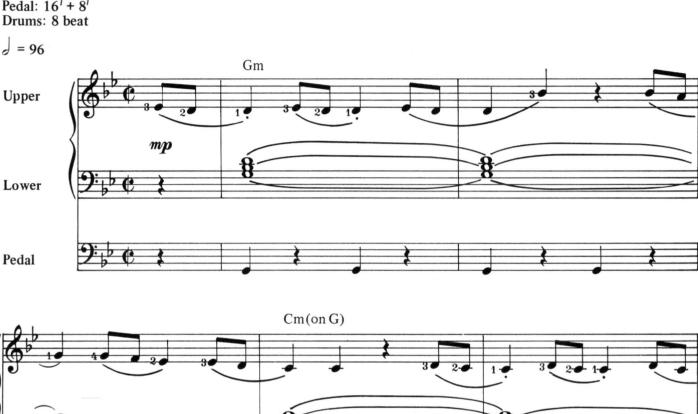

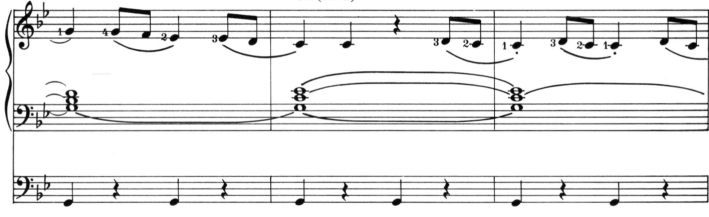

© Copyright 1992 Dorsey Brothers Music Limited, 8/9 Frith Street, London W1.
All Rights Reserved. International Copyright Secured.

stop drums

La Calinda

Composed by Frederick Delius.

© Copyright 1992 Dorsey Brothers Music Limited, 8/9 Frith Street, London W1.
All Rights Reserved. International Copyright Secured.

Moonlight Sonata

Composed by Ludwig Van Beethoven.

© Copyright 1992 Dorsey Brothers Music Limited, 8/9 Frith Street, London W1.
All Rights Reserved. International Copyright Secured.

73

Eine Kleine Nachtmusik

Composed by Wolfgang Amadeus Mozart.

Upper: string ensemble
Lower: flutes
Pedal: 16′ + 8′
Drums: 8 beat (or off)

© Copyright 1992 Dorsey Brothers Music Limited, 8/9 Frith Street, London W1.
All Rights Reserved. International Copyright Secured.

Berceuse

Composed by Gabriel Fauré.

Upper: flute
Lower: piano
Pedal: 16' + 8'
Drums: 8 beat

© Copyright 1992 Dorsey Brothers Music Limited, 8/9 Frith Street, London W1.
All Rights Reserved. International Copyright Secured.

stop drums

15831   7/93